CARROT
THE STARS

Written by : Régis Lejonc   Drawings : Riff Reb's
Based on an original story by : Thierry Murat

THE LAKES INTERNATIONAL COMIC ART FESTIVAL

Thanks to Carole Tait for the translation.

This English edition published by
The Lakes International Comic Art Festival
in partnership with On a Marché sur la Bulle,
Amiens - France
www.comicartfestival.com

Legal Deposit: August 2016
EAN: 978-1-5272-0025-8
Printed by Imprimerie Lesaffre in Belgium

First edition: 2010 - Éditions de la Gouttière
147b rue Dejean, 80000 Amiens - France
www.editionsdelagouttiere.com

AT NIGHT WE SLEEP AND OFTEN DREAM.
SOMETIMES WE EVEN HAVE WAKING DREAMS.

SOME DREAM OF LOVE
WHILST DANCING IN THE MOONLIGHT.
SOME DREAM OF THE IMPOSSIBLE.

AND SO IT IS WITH THIS RABBIT, THIS RABBIT SCIENTIST,
WHO DREAMS OF SOMETHING DAZZLING.

DAY AND NIGHT, HE SEARCHES, HE TRIES, HE EXPERIMENTS,
HE BUILDS CASTLES IN THE AIR
WHILE THE WORLD SLEEPS.

NIGHT AND DAY, HE CLEARS, SOWS AND RAKES...

HE HOES, PLOUGHS AND DIGS...

HE PLANTS, DRAINS, WEEDS AND WATERS...

ALL THIS HE DOES IN THE HOPE THAT THE FRUITS
OF HIS LABOUR WILL BE WORTHWHILE.

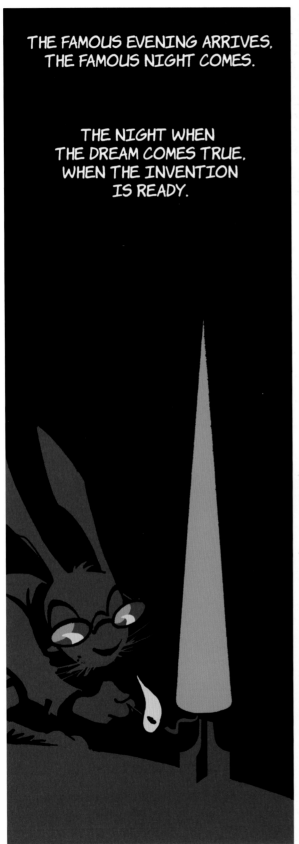

THE FAMOUS EVENING ARRIVES,
THE FAMOUS NIGHT COMES.

THE NIGHT WHEN
THE DREAM COMES TRUE,
WHEN THE INVENTION
IS READY.

THE CARROT SHOOTS
STRAIGHT UP IN THE AIR,
AS IF SUCKED UP
BY THE SKY.

EVERYONE WAKES AND WONDERS AND MARVELS.
NO ONE CAN BELIEVE THEIR EYES.
IT'S MARVELLOUS!
WHO HAS CREATED THIS WONDROUS THING?

THE NEXT DAY,
LIGHT IS SHED
ON THE MYSTERY.

SOON THE RABBIT SCIENTIST HITS THE HEADLINES...

HE'S ON THE RADIO.

HE'S FEATURED ON ALL KINDS OF TV SHOWS.

HE'S SHOWERED WITH
PRAISE AND COMPLIMENTS...

WITH OFFERS, PROJECTS
AND INCENTIVES.

THEY SAY "THANKS TO YOU,
THE WORLD PROGRESSES!"...

THEY SAY
"LET'S WORK TOGETHER FOR
THE COMMON GOOD",
THEY SAY "I WANT TO SEE
YOU IN MY OFFICE
TOMORROW!".

AND UNDER SUCH CIRCUMSTANCES,
RABBIT OR NOT,
YOU BELIEVE IT.

CONTRACTS ARE DRAWN UP,
CHEQUES ARE SIGNED, COPYRIGHTS ARE ASSIGNED.

THE INVENTION WILL BE MASS-PRODUCED.

IN NO TIME AT ALL, PATENT APPLICATIONS ARE FILED.
FACTORIES ARE BUILT, WORKERS ARE HIRED.
MASS PRODUCTION COMMENCES...

FINALLY, THE SCIENTIST
IS SIDE-LINED.
ALL HE HEARS IS
"LET US GET ON
WITH OUR WORK!"

"YOU'D BETTER GO HOME, WE'LL DEAL WITH EVERYTHING"
IT'S NO SURPRISE, HIS INVENTION IS
MAKING MILLIONS!

AND UNDER SUCH
CIRCUMSTANCES,
RABBIT OR NOT,
YOU HAVE TO GO.

HOWEVER,
NEWS OF THE CARROT'S
FORMIDABLE SUCCESS
REACHES THE PALACE.

THE SUN KING HIMSELF
SUMMONS THE
RABBIT SCIENTIST
EVERYONE IS
TALKING ABOUT.

MONEY
IS FOUND...

ASSISTANTS ARE HIRED...

STAFF ARE MOTIVATED AND RESULTS AWAITED!

DAY AFTER DAY AND NIGHT AFTER NIGHT,
THE RABBIT SEARCHES, HE TRIES, HE EXPERIMENTS.

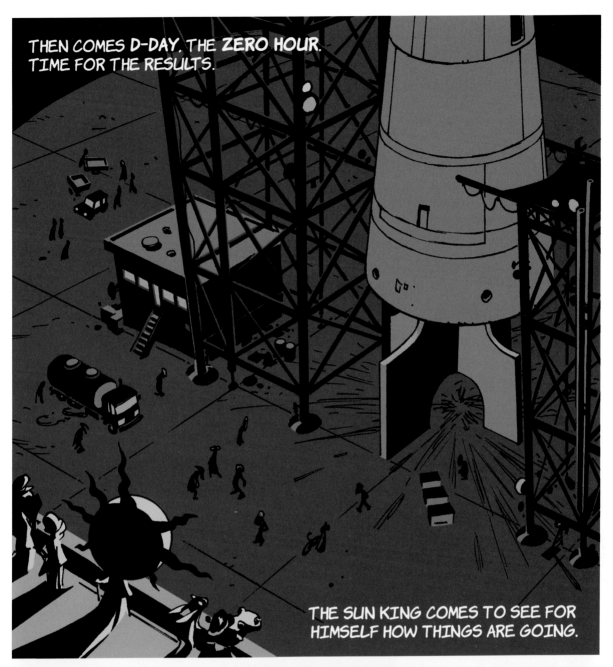

THEN COMES D-DAY, THE **ZERO HOUR**.
TIME FOR THE RESULTS.

THE SUN KING COMES TO SEE FOR
HIMSELF HOW THINGS ARE GOING.

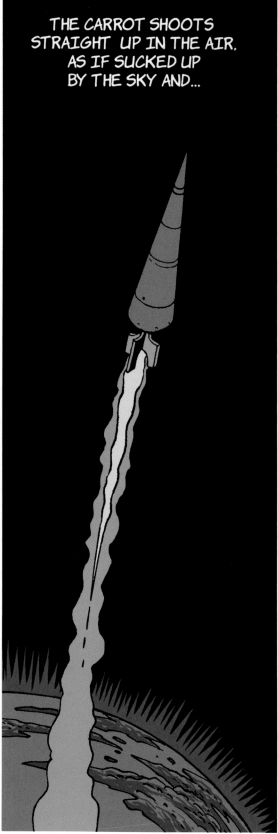

THE CARROT SHOOTS STRAIGHT UP IN THE AIR, AS IF SUCKED UP BY THE SKY AND...

BOOM!
THE MOON EXPLODES.

WHAT!
HOW IS **THAT** POSSIBLE?
THE RABBIT FEELS
BETRAYED.

THE SUN KING SEEMS PLEASED WITH HIMSELF.

APPARENTLY, THE MOON WAS HIS ENEMY.

THE SCIENTIST IS THANKED, THEN DISMISSED.

AND UNDER SUCH CIRCUMSTANCES, RABBIT OR NOT, YOU HAVE TO GO.

SO DON'T SURRENDER
YOUR DREAMS
TO JUST ANYONE.